goat
goldfish
girl
g
giant
goose
giraffe
P9-DBS-777

The **g**irl is **g**oing.

The **g**iant is **g**oing.

The **g**oat is **g**oing.

The **g**iraffe is **g**oing.

The **g**oose is **g**oing.

Everyone is **g**oing
to the football **g**ame.

My **g**randma says . . .

Good night!
Sleep tight!
Don't let
the bedbugs bite!